Robin Hood

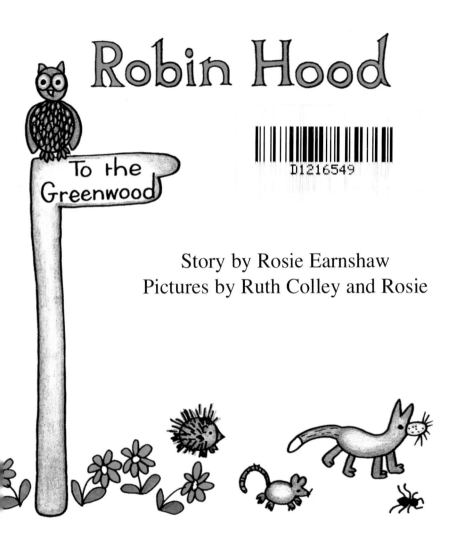

To the Greenwood

Story by Rosie Earnshaw
Pictures by Ruth Colley and Rosie

GEORGE JAMES BOOKS (LEICESTER)
1989

I

Robin Hood lived
deep in the
greenwood.

He lived with his
Merry Men in a den
in the big rocks.

Robin Hood and
his Merry Men
hid in the den.

The den was at the top
of a very big hill.

A little path
led up to
the den.

Robin had a green hat.
Robin had a green coat.
Robin had green pants.

The wood was green.
Robin was green too.
He hid in the wood.

Robin Hood was a good man.
He took money from the
rich men, to give to the
poor men.

He was not greedy.
No, he was not.
He was a good man.

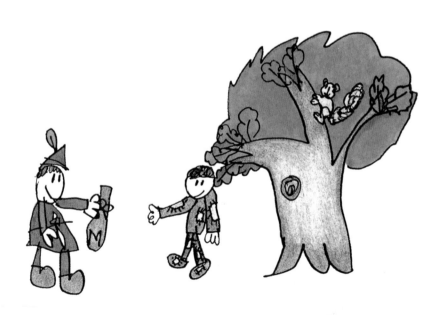

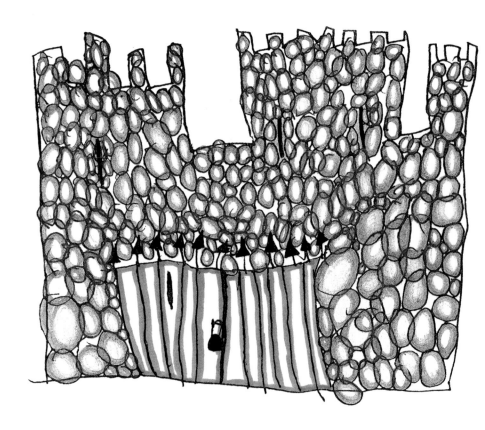

He hid from the
    Sheriff of Nottingham.

The Sheriff had a lot
    of soldiers in his castle.

It was a big castle.

The Sheriff had a lot
of money.

He kept his money in
big bags.

The Sheriff did not like
Robin Hood.

No, he did not.

"I will find Robin Hood,"
said the Sheriff.

"I will look for his den
in the Greenwood."

"I will find his Merry
Men too.

I will send my soldiers."

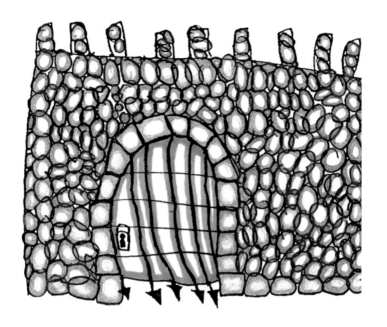

"I will put Robin Hood
and his Merry Men
in my castle.

I will lock them up.
I will."

In the Greenwood,
Robin and his Merry Men
sat on a big fat log.

"Let us sing a song,"
said Robin.

"Yes let us sing a song,"
said his Merry Men.

"Let us sing a song
    of the Greenwood."

It was a very good song.
    A very long song too.

"Let us go to sleep
    in the den," said Robin.

The Greenwood was very
dark.
The castle was dark.
The moon hid.

The Sheriff said to his soldiers,
"Good, it is dark. Let us
go and find Robin Hood
and his Merry Men."

The Sheriff of Nottingham
   left the castle.

The soldiers said,
   "No moon,
   It is very dark.
   We can not see very well."

The soldiers went on
in the dark.

A soldier fell in the pond.

A soldier sat in the mud.

A soldier lost his hat.

"It is too dark,"
the soldiers said.

"Go on," said the Sheriff,
"Go on, I must find
Robin Hood.

Go on, I must find his
Merry Men."

The animals in the
    Greenwood
    did not like the
    Sheriff of Nottingham.

"We will tell Robin Hood"
said the animals.

"We will tell him that the
Sheriff is in the
Greenwood."

"Let me help," said the frog.

"I will hop from my bog
and tell Robin Hood.

I can hop very well."

"Let me help," said the bat.

"I will fly by the den
and tell Robin Hood.

I can fly very well."

"Let me help," said the deer.

"I will jump on the rocks
    and tell Robin Hood.

I can jump very well."

"Let me help," said the fox.

"I will run up the path
and tell Robin Hood.

I can run very well."

The owl
and the
woodpecker
said,

"We have a plan.
It is a very good plan."
"I will hoot," said the owl.

"A very very big hoot.
Hoo - oo - oo - t.
Hoo - oo - oo - oo - t."

"I will tap on the tree,"
said the woodpecker.

"A very very long tap.
Tap - tap - tap - tap - tap.
Tap - tap - tap - tap - tap."

"Let me help too,"
said the little ant.

"I can nip a lot.
Nip - nip - nip - nip - nip.
Nip - nip - nip - nip - nip."

"I will help too,"
said the wee bee.

"See me buzz.
Buzz - buzz - buzz
Buzz - buzz - buzz."

The owl, the woodpecker,
   the ant and the bee said,

1 2 3

"Hoo - oo - oo - oo - oo - t.
   Tap - tap - tap - tap - tap.
   Nip - nip - nip - nip - nip.
   Buzz - buzz - buzz - buzz."

The soldiers ran.

The soldiers ran so fast
down the path,
by the rocks,
under the trees,
in the dark,
back to the big castle.

"Very good," said Robin
Hood.

"Very good," said the
Merry Men.

"Very good" said the frog,
the bat the deer, the
fox, the owl and the
woodpecker.

The little ant was asleep.

The bee buzzed off
to make some honey.

Copyright © Rosemary Smith 1987
Printed in England by
Easonprint, Mansfield Woodhouse, Notts.